Peppa's First Glasses

Peppa and George are outside playing with their friend Pedro Pony. They are busy jumping in muddy puddles.

Splash! Splosh! Splish!
"Ha! Ha! Ha!" Peppa giggles as she
jumps up and down.

"Argh! Ooh!" Pedro exclaims as he slips in a puddle and falls over. His glasses fly high into the air and land on the grass.

"Neigh! Where are my glasses?"
Pedro asks Peppa and George,
stumbling about. Pedro can't
see very well without them.

Peppa and George look for Pedro's glasses. George quickly finds them and tries them on.
"Silly George!" Peppa says.

She takes the glasses and gives them
back to Pedro. "Here they are."
"Thank you," says Pedro as he puts
them on.

"Pedro, why do you wear glasses?"
Peppa asks.
"I need to," replies Pedro. "My daddy
says so. He's an optician."

"What's an optician?" Peppa wonders.
Pedro explains, "An optician checks
that you can see clearly. He does an
eye test."

"Shall I give you an eye test?"
Pedro asks Peppa. Peppa agrees,
and Pedro leans in close.

"Hmmm, interesting," he says,
rubbing his chin. "Close one eye
and say what you can see."
"I can see George," Peppa says.
George snorts.

"Now, close both eyes," Pedro
instructs Peppa.
Peppa closes both her eyes.
"I can't see anything," Peppa says.

"Hmmm, can't see anything." Pedro
says. "I think you need glasses!"
Soon it is time for everyone to
go home.

Peppa and George go inside.
"Pedro gave me an eye test and I
need glasses," says Peppa. "When I
closed my eyes, I couldn't see."

"No one can see with their eyes closed,"
Mummy Pig explains. "But Pedro knows
all about glasses." Peppa sighs. "Ok,"
laughs Daddy Pig. "Let's take you to
the optician for a proper eye test."

Peppa and Mummy Pig are at the optician's. "What can I do for you?" Mr Pony asks Peppa.
"I need an eye test, please," Peppa replies, jumping up into his special chair.

"Of course," Mr Pony says. "Put these special glasses on and then look at the chart."

Mr Pony is going to test Peppa's eyes.

Mummy Pig helps Peppa try on some glasses while Mr Pony checks the test results. Some pairs look a little funny! "How about these heart-shaped ones?" Mummy Pig says.

"Wow! I like these ones, Mummy,"
says Peppa.
They both agree that Peppa looks
fantastic in the glasses.

Mr Pony comes back with the results.
"Good news: Peppa has perfect eyesight!"
"Oh! So I don't need glasses." Peppa
sighs disappointedly. "But I really
wanted some."